Curriculum Vision

Spelling Book 6

Sarah Lindsay

Curriculum Visions
Spelling

Teacher's Resource Book
There is a Teacher's Resource Book to accompany this Pupil Book.

Dedicated Web Site
There's more information about other great Curriculum Visions resources and a wealth of supporting material available at:
www.CurriculumVisions.com

Author
Sarah Lindsay

Art Director
Duncan McCrae

Senior Designer
Adele Humphries

Editors
Robert Anderson and Gillian Gatehouse

Illustrations
Mark Stacey

Designed and produced by
EARTHSCAPE EDITIONS

Printed in China by
WKT Company Ltd

This product is manufactured from sustainable managed forests. For every tree cut down at least one more is planted.

First published in 2006 by
Atlantic Europe Publishing Company Ltd

Text copyright © Sarah Lindsay 2006

The right of Sarah Lindsay to be identified as the author of this work has been asserted by her in accordance with the Copyright, Designs and Patents Act 1988.

Illustrations and design copyright © 2006 Atlantic Europe Publishing Company Ltd

Curriculum Visions Spelling Book 6
A CIP record for this book is available from the British Library.

ISBN-10: 1-86214-515-6
ISBN-13: 978-1-86214-515-3

Contents

soft c and g

exercise

apologise

bicycle	apologise	confidence	anthology
exercise	challenge	decision	contagious
innocent	original	democracy	courageous
receive	religion	necessary	imagination
science	vegetable	tolerance	outrageous

Finding words

A Write a word from the word list that matches each picture.

B

1 Underline the **soft c** or **soft g** in each of the words you have written.

2 Read aloud the words you have written.
What letter sounds do the **soft c** and **soft g** make?

Using words

One way of recognising **soft c** and **soft g** letters in a word is by looking at the letters following them.

A Sort the **soft c** words in the word list according to the letters following it. What do you notice?

Now sort the **soft g** words in the word list in the same way. What do you notice this time?

B Add two of your own **soft c** and **soft g** words to each of the columns.

You'll need to draw a table with three columns for the **soft c** words and the same again for the **soft g** words, like this...

ce	ci	cy

Puzzle corner

Connectives are words and phrases that are used to join clauses and sentences. Many connectives are compound words.

These are useful words to learn how to spell.

A Copy this passage and add the best connective from the box to fill each gap.

> furthermore   because   therefore

Mum, I think we should be allowed to go to bed later tonight _____ it is the weekend tomorrow. _____ we can sleep for longer in the morning. _____ we don't get to see our cousins very often _____ they live too far away. What do you think?

B Write Mum's response. Include the connectives in the box.

> although   whatever   because   consequently

Unit 2
silent letters

castle	autumn	campaign	conscious
design	knead	knickers	exhibition
island	knight	rhubarb	knowledge
honest	salmon	solemn	rhinoceros
wrong	scissors	subtle	wrath

Finding words

A Look at the picture. List all the words with silent letters found in the word list.

B Copy ten words found in the word list and circle their silent letters.

Using words

A Each of these words is a **homophone**.

Copy the words below and write a homophone for each one. Each homophone must have a silent letter.

> Remember, **homophones** are words which sound the same but have different meanings and/or spellings.

   1 rap   **2** ring

   3 sent   **4** which   **5** night   **6** right

   7 not   **8** boy   **9** rein   **10** new

B Choose four of the pairs of words.
Write each pair in a sentence.

Puzzle corner

A Copy this passage. Underline the words that are spelt incorrectly.

Ben waited for Meena outside her house. He coud see her in the kichen grabing a couple of apples. They had planed to wait all night in the garden shed until they came face to face with the gost. When lisening to the idea, their close frend Josh douted they would get a glimse and bet they were more likely to cach neumonia! Ben new seeing the gost was unlikely but was determined to give it a go. He felt nervous and excited as Meena ran out the house carrying the napsack.

B Write correctly each word that you have underlined.

Unit 3

able
ible
irresistible
comfortable

avoidable	accessible	available	audible
bearable	convertible	forgivable	gullible
comfortable	destructible	reliable	invincible
enjoyable	digestible	undeniable	irresistible
likeable	incredible	unmistakable	susceptible

Finding words

A Copy the sentences.

Fill each gap with a different **able** or **ible** word from the word list.

> You might need to check the definitions of some of these words in a dictionary before completing the sentences.

1 Jess found the pantomime very _____.
2 Grandpa sat in his _____ armchair and soon fell asleep.
3 The special effects during the magic show were _____.
4 Mark was _____; he thought the lady had really been cut in half!
5 Aimee enjoyed it when Mum put down the hood of her _____ car.
6 The ramp at the door made the library _____ to people in wheelchairs.
7 Dad's voice was just _____; the phone line was so bad.
8 There were plenty of tickets _____, so Dad bought four.

B Use each of these words in your own sentences.

1 avoidable   2 forgivable   3 irresistible

Using words

Be careful when you add the **able** or **ible** suffix to a word ending in one **e**. Usually you need to **drop the e** and then add the suffix.

| forgive | + | able | = | forgivable |

But… if there is a **soft c** or **soft g** before the **e**, the **e** needs to be kept and then the suffix added.

| trace | + | able | = | traceable |

> This is a useful rule to learn!

A Add **able** to these words.

| **1** believe | **2** enjoy | **3** change | **4** transfer |
| **5** manage | **6** argue | **7** debate | **8** service |

B Add **ible** to these words.

| **1** sense | **2** flex | **3** convert | **4** resist |
| **5** extend | **6** reverse | **7** collapse | **8** defense |

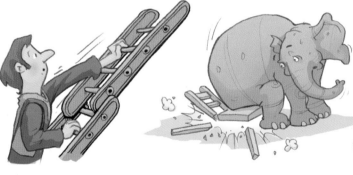

Puzzle corner

Words can be split into syllables.
Some syllables may have a vowel that is hard to hear.
This is known as an **unstressed vowel**.

| history | | his / tory |

A Copy each of these words, splitting them into syllables.

| **1** vegetable | **2** necessary | **3** dictionary | **4** diesel |
| **5** envelope | **6** interest | **7** entrance | **8** temperature |

B Now circle the unstressed vowel in each word, like this:

veg(e) / ta / ble

Unit 4

aero
auto
aqua

autopilot

aquarium

aeroplane

aerobatics	autobiography	aquaplane	aerodynamic
aerobics	autograph	aquarium	aeronautics
aerodrome	automatic	Aquarius	automation
aeroplane	automobile	aquatic	autonomous
aerosol	autopilot	aquatint	aqualung

Finding words

A Find seven words from the word list in this wordsearch.

Write the words you find.

B Now choose four of the more unusual words from the word list. Check their meanings in a dictionary and write out the definitions.

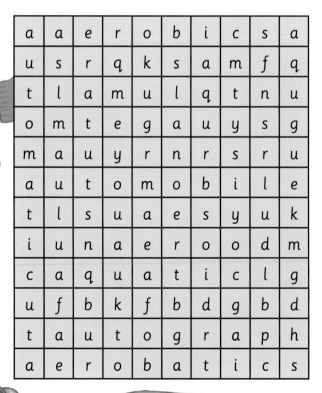

a	a	e	r	o	b	i	c	s	a
u	s	r	q	k	s	a	m	f	q
t	l	a	m	u	l	q	t	n	u
o	m	t	e	g	a	u	y	s	g
m	a	u	y	r	n	r	s	r	u
a	u	t	o	m	o	b	i	l	e
t	l	s	u	a	e	s	y	u	k
i	u	n	a	e	r	o	o	d	m
c	a	q	u	a	t	i	c	l	g
u	f	b	k	f	b	d	g	b	d
t	a	u	t	o	g	r	a	p	h
a	e	r	o	b	a	t	i	c	s

Using words

aero, auto and aqua are all **prefixes**. Understanding the meaning of the prefix can help us understand the word.

A **prefix** can change the meaning of a word.

> aero means **air**
> auto means **self**
> aqua means **water**

A Write what you think each of these words might mean.

    1 aquaplane   **2** aerogram   **3** autocue

B

1 Invent six of your own words, two for each of the prefixes studied in this unit. Write the words with their definitions.

2 Now write a short story including each of the words you have invented!

Here's a new word… **aerosleep** means sleeping while floating in the air!

Puzzle corner

Recognising similar words from the same word family can help your spelling.

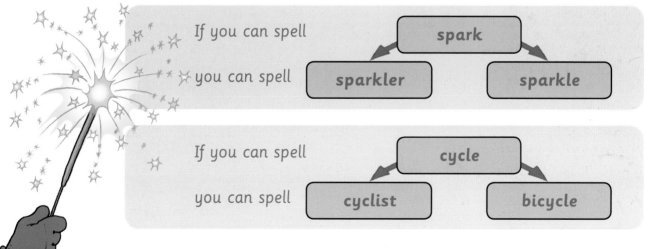

If you can spell **spark**

you can spell **sparkler** **sparkle**

If you can spell **cycle**

you can spell **cyclist** **bicycle**

A For each word below write two more words from the same word family.

    1 prison   **2** smart   **3** happy   **4** jump

B Find five words in your reading book that are members of word families. For each of the five words write as many other words from that word family as you can.

Unit 5

bi
con
co

coordinate

consult

bicycle

biannual	condense	coeducation	bicentenary
biceps	confront	coexist	congregation
bicycle	construct	cohabit	consensus
bifocal	consult	cooperate	coincidence
bisect	converge	coordinate	correspondent

Finding words

A Complete each sentence with a word from the word list.

1 Who can _____ the tallest tower using lego blocks?
2 Look at that man's arms – he has huge _____!
3 The police said if the criminals _____ and say who else was involved they might not go to prison.
4 The school magazine is _____ – it comes out twice a year.
5 It is always important to _____ your fears.
6 What a _____! I didn't know you were coming to the match too.
7 Go and get your _____, then we'll go to the park.
8 On Christmas Eve the church _____ was double its normal size.

B Now write four more words from the word list in your own sentences.

If you are unsure of the meanings of some of the words, check them in a dictionary!

Using words

bi, con and co are all **prefixes**.

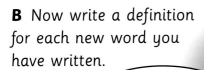

> **bi** means **twice, two**
> con means **with, together**
> **co** means **joint**

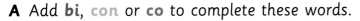

Understanding the meaning of the prefix can help us understand the word.

A Add **bi**, con or **co** to complete these words.

   1 lingual   **2** operative   **3** plane
   4 current   **5** operation   **6** spire

B Now write a definition for each new word you have written.

The prefix meanings above might help!

Puzzle corner

Our language has changed over the years.
There are many words that are no longer used and some which have slightly changed.

Did you know many verb endings have changed… for example 'he remains' was 'he remaineth'!

A Match the modern words with the old words.

comes	art
are	abides
lives	saith
to	hither
here	unto
says	cometh

B What do you think each of these words mean?

   1 wilt   **2** hath   **3** thither

Unit 6

graph
scope

telescope

photograph

autograph	horoscope	choreograph	endoscope
paragraph	microscope	monograph	kaleidoscope
photograph	telescope	telegraph	periscope

Finding words

A Write the words from the word list that you can find in the picture.

There are six to find!

B Write each word you have found in a sentence.

Using words

By adding a **suffix** to the end of a word it either changes its meaning or helps it 'fit' into a sentence.

The suffixes **graph** and **scope** are of Greek origin.

This is not an easy thing to do!

A Look carefully at the words using the **graph** and **scope** suffixes.

Write a meaning for each of the suffixes.

Check your answers with your teacher.

B

1 Now, knowing the meaning of the suffixes **graph** and **scope**, invent six of your own words using these suffixes.

Have you seen my **doublescope**? It's a toy that enables you to see two of everything!

2 Write a definition for each of your invented words.

Puzzle corner

Proper names or nouns are the special names of people, places or things.

The origins of many proper names have arisen for historical reasons.

Did you know that the word Monday is named after the moon and Sunday after the sun.

A The origins of many surnames are based on people's jobs. Describe what you think these children's ancestors might have done.

1 Dave Thatcher   **2** Katie Archer   **3** Tom Baker   **4** Jade Forester

5 Fred Shepherd   **6** Laila Smith

B Think about the surnames of other people in your class. Write what might be the origins of these surnames.

Unit 7

cc

occasion

accident

accent	accidentally	accomplice	accommodation
accept	account	accurate	accomplish
access	hiccup	occurrence	occupation
accident	occasion	successful	succinct
success	occupy	succulent	succumb

Finding words

A Which word am I?

1 I'm precise.
2 I am where people live.
3 I'm an unfortunate event.
4 I'm a sudden stop of breath.
5 I'm a job.
6 I'm your partner in a crime.
7 I'm a special event.
8 I'm a different pronunciation.

B Write a clue, like those above, for each of these **cc** words.

1 success
2 account
3 succulent
4 succinct

> If you are unsure of the meaning of any of these words, check them in a dictionary first. It will help you write a clue.

Using words

Being aware of word families can help you with your spelling.

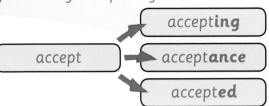

accepting

accept → acceptance

accepted

Did you know that in a **cc** word, if the second **c** is followed by an **e** or an **i**, the second **c** makes the **soft c** sound 's', as in ac**c**ident.

A dictionary might help!

A Write two more words that come from each of these word families.

1 accident	**2** occupy
3 access	**4** success
5 occur	**6** accommodate

How many different suffixes and prefixes have you used?

B Choose one of the word families you have made. Write each word from the word family into a different sentence showing you understand how each word should be used.

Puzzle corner

New words are always being added to our language as new things are invented and fashions change.

A Write down the words from the list below which you think have been introduced into our language in the last one hundred years.

B Write a definition for each of the new words.

mobile phone

broadband

fries

swimming costume

microchip

sunglasses

quad bike

television

compact disc

bread

car

computer game

Unit 8

tele
tri
oct

telescope **octopus** **tripod**

tele**pathic**	**tri**angle	oct**agon**	tele**scopic**
tele**phone**	**tri**cycle	oct**ahedron**	**tri**angular
tele**scope**	**tri**ple	oct**et**	**tri**athlon
tele**vise**	**tri**o	**Oct**ober	**tri**plicate
tele**vision**	**tri**pod	oct**opus**	oct**ogenarian**

Finding words

A Write the words from the word list that you can find in the picture.

This time there are seven to find.

B Choose five words from the word list, not found in the picture. Write each word in a sentence.

Using words

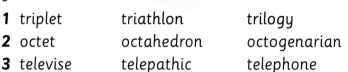

A Write a definition for each of these words. Use a dictionary to help you.

1 triplet   triathlon   trilogy
2 octet   octahedron   octogenarian
3 televise   telepathic   telephone

B Look at the definitions you have written. Write the meaning you think each prefix adds to each group of words.

1 tri   2 oct   3 tele

Think carefully about the **tele** prefix!

What do the prefixes **tri** and **oct** have in common?

Puzzle corner

Etymology is about looking at the history and origins of words. An **etymological dictionary** provides you with information on the origins of words, listed alphabetically.

Look carefully at these entries from an etymological dictionary.

toddle	c.1600, Scottish and northern British; reference to the word 'toddler' is first found in 1793
toffee	1825, southern British dialect; was 'taffy'; reference to 'toffee' is first found in 1862
trolley	1823, Suffolk dialect, probably from 'troll' (to roll)
tyre	1485, original spelling, then spelt 'tire'; returned to 'tyre' spelling in early 1800s in Great Britain

Answer these questions.

1 What was the original word for 'toffee'?
2 When was the word 'toddler' first used?
3 Which word changed its spelling to 'tire'?
4 Where is it thought the word 'toddle' first originated?
5 What is the significance of 'to roll' to the word trolley?
6 Which of the words has the earliest origin?

Unit 9

dge
age

smudge

garage

ba**dge**	**bandage**	cartri**dge**	**advantage**
e**dge**	**damage**	knowle**dge**	**discourage**
he**dge**	**garage**	misju**dge**	**encourage**
nu**dge**	**postage**	preju**dge**	**percentage**
sle**dge**	**sausage**	smu**dge**	**pilgrimage**

Finding words

A Write a word from the word list that matches each picture.

  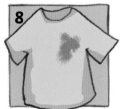 

B Use a dictionary to write a definition for each of these words.

1 prejudge   **2** pilgrimage   **3** discourage   **4** misjudge

Have you noticed that the words **prejudge** and **misjudge** have the same root, just a different prefix?

Using words

You need to remember that usually when a **suffix** is added to a word ending in **e**, the **e** is dropped if the suffix begins with a **vowel** or **y**.

Like this...
pledge ➡ pledging

A Copy and complete the table.

	ed	ing	er
manage			
lodge			
package			
sledge			

An exception to the rule is when the suffixes **ous** and **able** are added to **age** words.

Like this...
courage ➡ courageous

B Copy and complete the table.

Watch out! Not all the suffixes are used with each of these words.

	able	ment	ous
outrage			
advantage			
manage			

Puzzle corner

A **mnemonic** is a useful way of remembering tricky spellings. It can be a rhyme, an acronym or a saying.

An **acronym** is a word made from the initial letters of other words.

A Which words do each of these mnemonics help you spell?

1 **s**ome **p**eople **e**at **c**rumpets **i**n **a** **l**aundry
2 **b**ig **e**lephants **c**an **a**lways **u**nderstand **s**mall **e**lephants
3 **r**hyme **h**as **y**our **t**oes **h**opping **m**adly
4 **p**arrots **e**verywhere **o**ften **p**eel **l**ong **e**nvelopes

The best mnemonics are the ones **you** make up to help with the spellings **you** find tricky.

B Make up your own mnemonics for each of these words.

1 engine   2 February   3 awkward

Unit 10
gue

fatigue

tongue

league	catalogue	dialogue	analogue
tongue	fatigue	epilogue	monologue
vague	intrigue	prologue	synagogue

Finding words

A Complete each sentence with a word from the word list.

1 They really hoped to win the football _____ this year.

2 Matthew worshipped at the local _____ every Saturday morning.

3 Mia searched through the _____ for a new helmet.

4 Helen was hoping for a digital watch but she got an _____ one!

5 The _____ described the play as a comedy with a serious message.

6 The snake smelt the air with its _____.

7 Ben looked _____; he was thinking of something else while Tom talked to him.

8 Towards the end of the doubles tennis match there was urgent _____ between the losing tennis partners!

If you are unsure of the meanings of some of the words, check them in a dictionary.

B Now write three more words from the word list in your own sentences.

22

Using words

The origin of many words ending in **gue** is Greek or Latin. Many words that end in **logue** come from a Greek word meaning 'word' or 'speech'.

A Look at the words in the word list.
List all the words that are derived from the Greek word meaning **word** or **speech**. Check the words you have chosen in the dictionary.

B Look at these pairs of words.
Describe how they are different.

> 1 **prologue** and **epilogue**
> 2 **monologue** and **dialogue**
> 3 **Decalogue** and **catalogue**

Puzzle corner

Remember… all words can be split into syllables.
Some syllables may have a vowel that is hard to hear.
This is known as an **unstressed vowel**.

A Copy the words below. Divide each word into its syllables.
Tick ✔ the words with an unstressed vowel and cross ✘ those without.

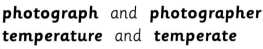

| photographer | cruel | secretary | miniature | lemonade |
| signature | photograph | temperate | temperature | |

B What do you notice about your answer for the words:

> **photograph** and **photographer**
> **temperature** and **temperate**

Unit 11

ex
sub

submerge

expand

exchange	**sub**heading	**ex**cept	**sub**conscious
exclaim	**sub**plot	**ex**clude	**sub**marine
exhaust	**sub**title	**ex**pire	**sub**merge
expand	**sub**way	**ex**plode	**sub**missive
extend	**sub**zero	**ex**terior	**sub**standard

Finding words

A Choose five words from the word list of whose meaning you are unsure.
Look these words up in a dictionary.

Copy the words and write their definitions.

B Find eight words from the word list in this wordsearch.

Write the words you find.

g	e	j	s	t	e	w	a	m	l
s	k	l	u	c	m	y	k	k	s
d	s	u	b	m	e	r	g	e	u
t	e	e	w	l	g	s	j	x	b
e	x	p	a	n	d	t	m	p	z
f	t	j	y	a	s	g	w	l	e
d	e	x	c	l	u	d	e	o	r
j	n	c	y	m	f	e	d	d	o
c	d	g	m	d	a	s	t	e	f
s	u	b	m	i	s	s	i	v	e

Using words

A Copy these prefixed words and underline the root in each one.

1 subtitle 2 subzero
3 exchange 4 export
5 submarine 6 substandard
7 exclaim 8 subconscious

Remember a **prefix** can sometimes be added to change the meaning of a word – **ex** means out of, from or away **sub** means under or below

B Write each of the words above in a sentence. Take note of how the meaning of the root changes when the prefix is added to it.

Puzzle corner

I challenge you to be a prefix/ suffix detective!!

A Look at these prefixes or suffixes. Each adds a unit of meaning to a root. Do some investigative work to find the meaning of each prefix or suffix, including its origin.

1 tri 2 auto 3 able
4 ful 5 less

B Write three example words for each of the above prefixes or suffixes.

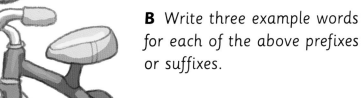

Unit 12

ic

comic

allergic

comic	**allerg**ic	**electron**ic	**aesthet**ic
cubic	**angel**ic	**ideal**istic	**character**istic
picnic	**bion**ic	**prehistor**ic	**gymnast**ic
fabric	**frant**ic	**realist**ic	**hygien**ic
tragic	**histor**ic	**scen**ic	**optimist**ic

Finding words

A Write a word from the word list that matches each picture.

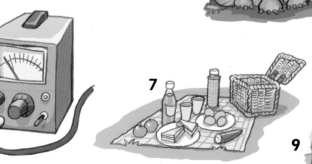

B Look at the opening picture. Write a few sentences telling the story in the comic. Use as many **ic** words from the word list as you can.

I think I could use five **ic** words.

Using words

Most words ending in **ic** are adjectives.

athlete   athlet**ic**

Some words ending in **ic** are nouns.

com**ic**

Sometimes the **ic** suffix is added to a **noun** to change it into an **adjective**.

A Copy and sort these words into nouns and adjectives.

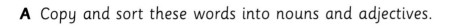

poetic	gigantic	rhythmic	traffic	allergic
picnic	music	hygienic		fabric
robotic	angelic	mechanic	microscopic	

B Now write the root of each of the adjectives you have listed.

Puzzle corner

One good turn deserves another.

A **proverb** is a saying that has been used for many years.

A Copy and complete each of these proverbs with a word from the box.

one	served	leap	another	perfect	lie

1 One good turn deserves _____.
2 First come, first _____.
3 Two heads are better than _____.
4 Look before you _____.
5 Let sleeping dogs _____.
6 Practice makes _____.

B Write what you think each of these proverbs mean.

1 Every cloud has a silver lining.

2 Better late than never.

Unit 13

ous

infectious

cautious

anxious	cautious	ambitious	courageous
curious	delicious	hilarious	instantaneous
furious	envious	infectious	miscellaneous
obvious	religious	mysterious	simultaneous
serious	spacious	suspicious	spontaneous

Finding words

A Look at the expression on each face.

Write the word from the word list that best describes it.

1 2 3 4

5

6

B Copy the sentence below six times. Each time add one of the words from **A**, then complete the sentence by describing your feelings about different things.

I feel _____ about _____.

Using words

The suffix **ous** is sometimes added in the forms **ious** or **eous**. Here are a few rules to help you.

- **ous** follows a **consonant** or a **silent e**, which is dropped.

  | nerve | → | nerv**ous** |

- **ious** is added when the word either ends in **ion** or **y** or after a **soft c**.

  | fury | → | fur**ious** |

- **eous** is added when the **e** sounds **ee** or to keep a **g soft**.

  | advantage | → | advantag**eous** |

A Make adjectives of each of these words by adding **ous**, **ious** or **eous**.

1 fame   **2** mountain   **3** religion
4 outrage   **5** mystery   **6** vary
7 melody   **8** victory   **9** suspicion

B Check each word in a dictionary, so that you are sure you have spelt each one correctly.

> Mark your own work. Rewrite the word correctly if you have misspelt it.

Puzzle corner

Words in our language change over time.

A Link each of the words below with its original meaning.

1	trainer	a tree
2	wicked	to hit repeatedly
3	cool	fine strands
4	bread	a person who trains
5	web	nasty
6	box	break
7	flog	cold
8	snap	a food

B Now write another more recent meaning for each of the words in **A**. The pictures will give you some clues.

Unit 14

inter
micro

international

micro**light**

interact	**micro**chip	**inter**cept	**micro**circuit
intercom	**micro**film	**inter**mingle	**micro**electronics
interlink	**micro**light	**inter**national	**micro**meter
internet	**micro**scope	**inter**sect	**micro**scopic
interval	**micro**wave	**inter**view	**micro**surgery

Finding words

A Write the five words from the word list that you can find in the picture.

B Write each of these words in a sentence.

    1 interact   **2** microlight

    3 interlink   **4** microfilm

If you aren't sure what these words mean, check them in a dictionary.

Using words

inter and **micro** are both prefixes. Understanding the meaning of the prefix can help us understand the word.

> The words in this unit can be quite hard to understand. If you look at the prefix and root word separately it can make understanding (and spelling) the word easier.

> **inter** means **between, among**
> **micro** means **small**

A Write your own definition for each of these words.

1 intermingle 2 microcircuit
3 international 4 micrometer
5 intersect 6 microsurgery

> Can you invent some of your own words using the **inter** and **micro** prefixes? Write their definitions.

B Now look up each word in a dictionary. Copy the definition. How many of the words did you define correctly?

microburger means a very small, snack-sized burger!

Puzzle corner

When we **argue** a point of view there are some words and phrases that are useful to know.

> An **argument** is…
> • a discussion involving disagreement
> • a reason put forward

A Copy and complete the gaps in Kate's argument with words or phrases from the box.

> **in my opinion   consequently   furthermore   in conclusion   I believe**

_____ we shouldn't have to wear a school uniform to our school. _____ it would be more fun to decide from a variety of clothes and colours, _____ allowing children to be more individual. _____, buying a school uniform can be very expensive and not all parents can afford it. _____ I think it would be worth asking all parents and pupils at the school to gauge their opinion.

B Write a response to Kate's argument. Argue **for** keeping school uniform. Underline any 'argument' words or phrases you have used.

Unit 15
dd

saddle

ladder

cuddle	adder	addition	addiction
middle	ladder	address	additive
muddle	sudden	midday	Buddhism
saddle	wedding	suddenly	Buddhist

Finding words

A Write a word from the word list that matches each picture.

1

2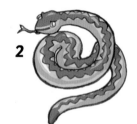

3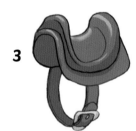

4

5 ?

6

7 2+2

8

9

B Look at the first column in the word list.
Each word ends in **le**.

List as many **dd** words that end in **le**
as you can.

> I managed to find thirteen, including the four in the word list!

Using words

Some **dd** words have become **dd** words because a suffix has been added. Remember, we often double the last letter when adding a suffix.

The rule to remember is:
if a word ends in a **short vowel** and a **d**, then the **d is doubled** when a suffix beginning with a vowel is added.

$$\boxed{\text{hi\textbf{dd}en}} = \boxed{\text{hid}} + \boxed{\text{the \textbf{en} suffix}}$$

A Write the root of each of these **dd** words.

1 wedding	**2** madden	**3** padded
4 plodding	**5** prodded	**6** skidding
7 maddest	**8** shredded	**9** nodding

B Complete these word sums.

1 wed + ed	**2** sad + en	**3** shred + er
4 mad + ness	**5** nod + ing	**6** bid + able
7 mad + er	**8** pad + ing	**9** sad + ly

Watch out! Not all words need the **d** doubled when the suffix is added.

Puzzle corner

Understanding and learning **spelling rules** can help improve your spelling.

A Read each of these spelling rules. Write two words that are an example of each of these spelling rules.

1 The letter **q** is always followed by the letter **u**.

2 **i** comes before **e** except after **c**, or when the sound is not **ee**.

3 Words usually end in **y** when they sound **ee** or **i**.

4 Words that sound **k** after a short vowel sound are usually spelt **ck**.

B Learn these spelling rules!

Unit 16

ist
ian

soloist

musician

artist	**histor**ian	**violin**ist	**amphib**ian
dentist	**magic**ian	**lingu**ist	**comed**ian
motorist	**music**ian	**novel**ist	**electric**ian
soloist	**optic**ian	**opportun**ist	**pedestr**ian
tourist	**politic**ian	**scient**ist	**technic**ian

Finding words

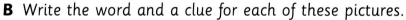

A What am I?

1 I pull rabbits from hats.
2 I stand alone in front of an orchestra.
3 I check canines!
4 I look back in time.
5 I light up rooms.
6 I sit in the Houses of Parliament.
7 I sit and think and write.
8 I visit new places.

B Write the word and a clue for each of these pictures.

1 **2** **3**

34

Using words

A Add the **ist** or **ian** suffix to each of these roots.

Check each word in a dictionary to be sure you have spelt it correctly.

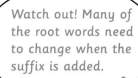

Watch out! Many of the root words need to change when the suffix is added.

1 history	**2** technical	**3** organ
4 botany	**5** India	**6** Buddha	**7** Australia
8 optic	**9** Christ

B Choose five of the words you have made in **A**.

Write each word in an amusing sentence.

Puzzle corner

Remember, a **mnemonic** is a way of learning a spelling you find difficult.

This might include the use of acronyms, rhymes or sayings!

separate

A List six words you frequently get wrong.

B Write a mnemonic for each of the words you have listed.

Make each mnemonic as amusing or strange as possible. This will help you remember it!

Look at work you have previously written to help pinpoint words that would be useful for you to spell correctly.

Unit 17

or
ar

visitor

guitar

actor	beggar	calculator	calendar
doctor	burglar	conqueror	familiar
sailor	guitar	instructor	irregular
visitor	popular	professor	particular
warrior	similar	radiator	perpendicular

Finding words

A Write a word from the word list that matches each picture.

B Write a few sentences about the picture above that includes at least six words from the word list.

Using words

All these words come from the same word family.

burglar	→	burgled	burglars	burgle	burglary

Always watch out for words from the same word family – it can help you with your spelling.

A Write as many words as you can from each of these word families. A dictionary might help.

1 calculator   **2** beggar   **3** instructor

4 familiar   **5** circular   **6** popular

B Using the **burglar** word family above, write each word from the word family into a short passage.

Puzzle corner

A Copy the words. Mark the correct words with a tick and the others with a cross.

Please will you mark my spelling test? I don't think I've done very well!

importent ☐   **children** ☐

swiming ☐   **suddnly** ☐

different ☐   **particuler** ☐

imediate ☐   **questionaire** ☐

jewellry ☐   **exaggerate** ☐

Next to the words that are wrong, write the correct spelling. Use a dictionary to help if you need to.

B Look through your work.

Write down correctly five words you have misspelt.

Unit 18

ary
ery
ory

direct**ory**

lib**rary**

slipp**ery**

di**ary**	batt**ery**	conservat**ory**	extraordin**ary**
diction**ary**	deliv**ery**	direct**ory**	necess**ary**
gloss**ary**	gall**ery**	introduct**ory**	jewell**ery**
lib**rary**	myst**ery**	satisfact**ory**	station**ery**
secret**ary**	slipp**ery**	vict**ory**	contradict**ory**

Finding words

A Complete each sentence with a word from the word list.

1 Hannah fell awkwardly on the _____ floor.

2 Mrs McKinley's class visited the local _____ in search of information on their home town.

3 "A special _____ for Jessica! Is it your birthday?", the postman asked.

4 Craig loved his _____ karate session; he was definitely going to finish the course.

5 The school _____ counted the dinner money carefully.

6 Nan and Grandad's new _____ added an extra room to their house.

7 Najib's work was _____ but his Mum and Dad knew he could do better!

8 Pete, the mechanic, thought our car wouldn't start because the _____ was flat.

B Now write three more words from the word list in your own sentences.

A **root word** is the word to which a **prefix** or **suffix** is added to make another word.

Using words

A Write the root of each of these words.

1 introductory	**2** contradictory	**3** conservatory
4 discovery	**5** machinery	**6** nursery
7 boundary	**8** burglary	**9** celebratory

B Add **ary**, **ery** or **ory** to each of these to make a word.

1 ordin___	**2** brib___	**3** necess___
4 hist___	**5** station___	**6** surg___
7 imagin___	**8** annivers___	**9** compuls___

One of the above groups of letters can have two of the suffixes added to it to make two different words. Write them both down.

If you are unsure which word ending to add, don't worry... just check the word in the dictionary.

Puzzle corner

Open your dictionary at any page. Write the page number.

Now answer the following questions.

1 Write the first word on the page.
2 Write a noun found on the page.
3 Write a word that has more than one definition.
4 Write a word that you think you will find on the following page of the dictionary.
5 Write a verb found on the page.
6 Write a plural of a word found on the page.
7 Write the definition of a word found on the page.

You will need a dictionary to complete this Puzzle corner.

Unit 19

words to watch

potatoes

bargain

among	character	chimneys	desperately
bargain	excellent	description	encyclopedia
minute	probably	excitement	immediately
potatoes	pyjamas	foreign	permanent
quarter	surprise	tomorrow	temperature

Finding words

A Each of these short words can be found in a word from the word list. Write the longer word and then underline the short word found in it.

him **c<u>him</u>neys**

1 art	**2** nut	**3** cell
4 reign	**5** man	**6** jam
7 rob	**8** script	**9** rate

B Write all the short words you can find in each of these longer words.

1 potatoes	**2** tomorrow
3 excitement	**4** bargain

Using words

A Each of the following pictures is of a 'word to watch'. Write the word to match each picture.

> None of these words can be found in the word list!

1 e_____

2 F_____

3 r_____

4 s_____

5 l_____

6 m_____

7 y_____

8 l_____

9 a_____

B Now check each word you have just written in a dictionary. Tick the words you spelt right.

Rewrite the words correctly if you have spelt them wrong.

Puzzle corner

Spelling rules are a useful tool in helping us learn spellings.

One rule can apply to many, many words!

> It is worth remembering rules, but watch out... there are usually exceptions to each rule!

A Write a rule you associate with each of these words. The letters in bold give you a clue as to which rule each word highlights.

   1 rec**ei**ve   **2** sq**u**irrel   **3** happ**i**ly

   4 run**n**ing   **5** kni**ves**   **6** pac**k**age

B Write another word to illustrate each of the rules you have written in **A**.

Unit 20
nn

funnel

tunnel

channel	annual	announce	annihilate
flannel	connect	connection	annotate
funnel	dinner	innocent	innovation
kennel	funny	minnow	questionnaire
tunnel	scanner	tonne	unnecessary

Finding words

A Which word am I?

1 I'm a meal you eat.
2 I join two or more items.
3 I'm a dog's home.
4 I'm free from guilt.
5 I happen once a year.
6 I'm not needed.
7 I am a ditch that holds water.
8 I'm a completely new idea.

B Write a clue for each of these **nn** words.

1 minnow 2 funny
3 annotate 4 annihilate

If you are unsure of the meaning of any of these words, check them in a dictionary first — it will help you write a clue.

Using words

A Write one or more words that rhyme with each of the following words.

1 sunny **2** funnel **3** scanner

4 thinner **5** tanning **6** spinning

The rhyming words must also have a double n!

B Now use each group of rhyming words in an amusing sentence.

The sailor's flannel fell into the Channel!

Puzzle corner

Similes and **metaphors** are ways of describing a subject.

A **simile** is when a subject is **compared** to something else.

A **metaphor** is when a subject is **said to be** something else.

"The ballet dancer is as graceful as a swan."

"The wind danced through the field of oats."

A Complete each of these similes. The pictures will help.

1 as quick as a _____

2 as cool as _____

3 as dark as _____

4 as fast as a _____

5 as sleepy as a _____

6 as white as _____

B Write a metaphor describing the subjects below.

1 snow **2** candy floss **3** a flooding river

Unit 21
ise

exercise	advise	advertise	emphasise
organise	devise	despise	franchise
promise	excise	disguise	improvise
realise	prise	dramatise	merchandise
surprise	revise	practise	synchronise

Finding words

A Complete each sentence with a word from the word list.

1 Veejay was shocked when he walked into the room, but he loved his _____ party!

2 The detective was wearing a _____, so that nobody would recognise him.

3 Kerry had to _____ for her spelling test.

4 Class 6 had to _____ the disco they were running to raise money for the homeless.

5 David's dad needed to do plenty of _____ to train for the marathon.

6 The twins had to _____ open the lid to get to the hidden sweets.

7 Helen and Laura decided to _____ their watches to be sure they met each other at the correct time.

8 Ben asked the shopkeeper if he could _____ the bring-and-buy sale in his shop window.

B Now write three more words from the word list in your own sentences.

If you are unsure of the meanings of some of the words, check them in a dictionary!

Using words

Look carefully at these words.

- Some of these words end in **ise** because the **ise** suffix has been added to the root.

  improve   improv**ise**

  - Some are just words that end in **ise** – for example pr**ise**

civilise   advise   exercise   emphasise   dramatise   revise
advertise   disguise   legalise   surprise   organise   characterise

A Copy and complete this table, adding each word in the correct column.

Words ending in **ise**	Words with the **ise** suffix

It is important to know the difference between each of these words, so you know which spelling to use when!

B Find the difference between each of these homophones.

1 pract**ise** and pract**ice**
2 dev**ise** and dev**ice**

Puzzle corner

Playing games with words can help you with their spellings!

Copy and complete this crossword. Each clue is for a word with double letters.

Across
1 a horse's foot
3 to embrace
4 to see
5 a small statue

Down
1 a sharp sudden noise from the mouth
2 another word for violin
6 nasty or sharp tasting

45

Unit 22
ive

expensive

distinctive

attractive	alternative	destructive	argumentative
detective	decorative	disruptive	cooperative
impressive	inventive	distinctive	defective
protective	expensive	excessive	offensive
talkative	explosive	supportive	persuasive

Finding words

A Find eight words from the word list in this wordsearch.

Write the words you find.

B Now choose four of the more unusual words from the word list.

Check their meanings in a dictionary and write out the definitions.

f	i	n	v	e	n	t	i	v	e	g	s
p	t	c	e	t	a	g	d	w	e	d	u
l	p	a	l	d	t	i	l	v	x	o	p
v	f	w	l	n	t	s	i	s	c	f	p
a	w	i	a	k	r	s	e	r	e	f	o
r	i	g	f	r	a	p	f	n	s	e	r
n	a	u	c	u	c	t	v	w	s	n	t
v	s	c	s	l	t	i	i	e	i	s	i
c	a	r	u	r	i	f	n	v	v	i	v
i	e	v	l	e	v	s	v	e	e	v	e
p	p	r	o	t	e	c	t	i	v	e	p
s	j	s	t	k	v	f	e	v	d	u	k

Using words

attractive

protective

detective

offensive

Did you know the **ive** suffix means 'one who' or 'that which is', when added to a word?

A List five more **ive** words that can't be found in the word list.

B Now use the five words you have listed and **all** the words from the word list in a short, amusing passage.

You can write about anything you like, but your challenge is that you have to use all the words in as short a passage as possible!

Puzzle corner

Over time more and more things and expressions are being invented. New words are invented to give a name to these new things!

cheese + hamburger = **cheeseburger**

A How do you think each of these words came about?

1 dogsbody **2** heliport
3 workaholic **4** smog

B Invent your own word for each of these.
  1 A word describing someone who doesn't like parties!
  2 A word describing a chocolate and egg sandwich!
  3 A word describing someone who always speaks backwards!

Spelling Challenge

Write a word that uses each of these sounds or letter patterns.

You have practised all the sounds and letter patterns in this book!

1 soft c, soft g
2 a silent letter
3 able, ible
4 aero, auto, aqua
5 bi, con, co
6 graph, scope
7 cc
8 tele, tri, oct
9 dge, age
10 gue
11 ex, sub
12 ic
13 ous
14 inter, micro
15 dd
16 ist, ian
17 or, ar
18 ary, ery, ory
19 nn
20 ise
21 ive

Well done, you have now finished this book. We hope it has helped you with your spellings.